NATU

AIR-PU
HOUSEPLANTS
and Healthy Housekeeping

N H Hawes

Hammersmith Health Books
London, UK

First published in 2017 by Hammersmith Health Books – an imprint of
Hammersmith Books Limited
4/4A Bloomsbury Square, London WC1A 2RP
www.hammersmithbooks.co.uk

Reprinted 2017

Note: No book can replace the diagnostic expertise and medical advice
of a trusted physician. Please be certain to consult your doctor before making any
decisions that affect your health or extreme changes to your diet, particularly if
you suffer from any medical condition or have any symptom that may require
treatment. Whilst the advice and information in this book are believed to be true
and accurate at the date of going to press, neither the author nor the publisher
can accept any legal responsibility or liability for any errors or omissions that
may have been made.

British Library Cataloguing in Publication Data: A CIP record of this book is
available from the British Library.

ISBN (print edition): 978-1-78161-083-1
ISBN (ebook): 978-1-78161-084-8

Commissioning editor: Georgina Bentliff
Cover design by: Julie Bennett, Bespoke Publishing Ltd
Typeset by: Julie Bennett, Bespoke Publishing Ltd
Production: Helen Whitehorn, Path Projects Ltd
Printed and bound by: TJ International Ltd

Contents

	About Nature Cures	4
1.	Introduction	5
2.	Household pollutants	7
3.	A to Z of household pollutants	8
4.	The A to Z of air-purifying houseplants	19
5.	Summary – which plants are best for which problems	78
6.	Other plants toxic to animals and young children	80
7.	A note about fungus gnats	86
8.	Other benefits of growing plants in the home	88
9.	Natural air fresheners	88
10.	Natural homemade cleaners	90
11.	How to use white vinegar	105
12.	Index	108

About Nature Cures

This pocketbook is a guide to natural ways to treat health issues. The information is drawn from my website www.naturecures.co.uk and my comprehensive book *Nature Cures: The A to Z of Ailments and Natural Foods*, available from www.hammersmithbooks.co.uk. For more detail about the nutrients and foods listed in this pocketbook, please do refer to these sources.

In both this book and my comprehensive works the sources of the information I've used are too numerous to list without at least doubling the size; if there is any fact or recommendation that is of concern, please do contact me via www.naturecures.co.uk.

This pocketbook represents a compilation of years of research but is no substitute for visiting a qualified health practitioner so please do consult such, especially your doctor with regard to any prescription medications, before making signficant changes to your diet, lifestyle or health regime.

Other titles in the series include
Let Roots Be Your Medicine
Grow Your Own Health Garden
Nature's Colour Codes

Introduction

In the late '80s, NASA scientists studied houseplants as a way of purifying the air in space facilities because the equipment used on the station, and even the astronauts themselves, produce gases and chemicals that can become concentrated and toxic over time. They were 'over the moon' to discover that several plants filter out common volatile chemical compounds and these plants can also help clean the indoor air down here on Earth, which is typically far more polluted than outdoor air.

Plants absorb some of the particulates from the air at the same time that they take in carbon dioxide, which is then processed into oxygen through what is called 'photosynthesis'. Photosynthesis is a two-step process, and the first step is when water is converted into oxygen. This first step directly requires light energy, which is captured by the photosynthetic pigments, mainly chlorophyll, in plant stems and leaves during daylight hours. The chlorophyll converts light energy (photons) into chemical energy, in the form of high-energy electrons. This chemical energy is used in the photosynthetic reaction centres to split two water molecules, producing four electrons, four protons, and two oxygen atoms, which combine to form oxygen gas (O_2). The chemical energy captured in step one is then used in step two of photosynthesis - that is, to convert carbon dioxide (CO_2) into carbohydrates (glucose). This glucose is then used in plant respiration or converted into starch and stored.

Most flowers and plants, except holy basil and mother-in-law's tongue, stop producing oxygen after dark and release carbon dioxide instead through respiration, though only at a minimal level. When plants photosynthesise, during daylight hours, most of them emit six molecules of oxygen and one of glucose for every six molecules of carbon dioxide they consume. When they respire, at night, this is reversed but since plants respire at a slower rate than they photosynthesise, there is a net gain of two to three molecules of oxygen per cycle. It is therefore perfectly safe to have a few plants in the bedroom at night. Holy basil and mother-in-law's tongue are two plants that are especially beneficial to have in the bedroom.

Houseplants can reduce, and even prevent, 'sick building syndrome', symptoms of which can include allergies, eye, ear and nasal irritations, dizziness, headaches and nausea. They can also reduce the risk of contracting colds and other viruses, decrease blood pressure, lift the mood, reduce mental fatigue and improve sleep. NASA research suggests having at least one plant per nine square metres (approximately100 square feet) of home or office space.

Growing plants in the home can be very beneficial to the health because not only can they remove airborne contaminants but some are also nutritious herbs for both medicinal and culinary use. Many also have volatile oils which can be used to clean the home and the body (see page 90) and most are safe to use on pets. However, there are some plants that are poisonous to young children and pets or livestock and this is also covered on page 80.

Household pollutants

Solvents in glues, paints and varnishes commonly used in the production of carpets, drywall (plasterboard) and pressed wood furniture, such as toluene and formaldehyde, are pollutants in most homes. Over 40 volatile organic compounds (VOCs) have been identified that come from modem appliances such as computers, monitors and televisions. The detrimental effects of indoor air pollution have been associated with a 74 per cent increase in asthma between 1980 and 1994 and children under the age of five in the United States have experienced an increase of 160 per cent. Studies have shown that reduced ventilation and increased energy efficiency in modem buildings and homes may be responsible for this.

There has been a fivefold increase in asthma in Taiwan over 20 years; and a 30-fold increase in the condition in medical facilities in Japan over 30 years. Likewise, 15 per cent of the population of Australia, New Zealand and the Pacific Islands now suffer from asthma. Indoor air pollution has also been linked to increased prevalence of Parkinson's disease, brain tumours, other nervous system disorders multiple chemical sensitivity and skin disorders.

The A to Z of house-hold pollutants

The chemicals below can build-up in the system and produce many health issues after prolonged exposure, especially for those who are unwell, elderly or very young whose body cannot easily eliminate toxins from the system. Those leading a sedentary lifestyle are also at risk as physical activity helps the body to decontaminate itself.

The A to Z of plants that can help against them generally and/or specifically starts on page 19 and for a quick guide relating to specific pollutants to specific plants see page 78. As noted already, all houseplants are potentially beneficial but only the 29 in the A to Z have been systematically researched.

Ammonia

Ammonia is found in refrigerators, cleaning products, dyes, fertilisers and textiles and can cause asthma, lung damage, rapid weak pulse and restlessness.

NOTE: Never mix ammonia with bleach. This causes the release of toxic chlorine gas which can be deadly.

Benzene

Dichlorobenzene and ethylbenzene are found in carpets, detergent, dyes, explosives, furniture, glue, ink, paint, petrol, pharmaceuticals, plastics, rubber and varnishes. Benzene is an irritant to the eyes and sinuses and is also known to cause chromosomal aberrations and leukaemia in humans. Chronic exposure to even low-levels causes drowsiness, headaches, loss of appetite, nervousness, psychological disturbances and diseases of the blood, such as anaemia and bone marrow disease. Acute inhalation of high levels of benzene can cause blurred vision, dizziness, euphoria, headache, irregular heartbeat, liver and kidney damage, nausea, paralysis, respiratory disorders, tremors, weakness and unconsciousness. Repeated skin contact with benzene causes blistering, dermatitis, dryness and inflammation.

Brominated flame retardants

Brominated flame retardants are chemicals that are used to slow down the rate of burning and are now linked to memory loss, low sperm counts, infertility in women, hyperactivity, learning difficulties and skin and nerve problems. They are found in soft furnishings, sofas, carpets, rugs, computer casings, DVD players and mobile phones.

Butane

Butane is used as lighter fluid and in butane torches. It is also sold in small bottles for cooking and may be blended with propane. It is also used as an aerosol propellant. Butane is a euphoric, so it is often abused as an inhalant but is dangerous due to the side effects of asphyxia, cardiac arrhythmia and spasms in the muscles of the airways in the lungs and is the cause of death in 55 per cent of the cases related to inhaling solvents and commonly called 'sudden sniffer's death'.

Chemical combinations

There are certain substances that should never be mixed together as the chemicals produced can damage to the eyes, lungs and skin and, in some cases, cause dangerous explosions. Often people mix shop-bought cleaning products unaware of the dangers of doing so. The following combinations should particularly be avoided.

- Baking soda and vinegar
- Bleach and ammonia
- Chlorine, bleach and vinegar
- Hydrogen peroxide and vinegar
- Rubbing alcohol and bleach.

Cleaning products

Many cleaning products contain chemicals linked to anxiety, asthma, birth defects, cancer, depression, hair loss, developmental disability and cancer. Oven cleaner contains corrosive lye which can burn the eyes and skin. Furniture polish is highly inflammable, and can cause cancer. Natural cleaning products easily made from plants that can be grown in the home are listed on page 90 of this pocketbook.

Decane
Decane is a chemical found in cove-based wall coverings, glue, paraffin, petrol and rubber flooring. Decane can cause defatting of the skin and dermatitis, corneal damage, dizziness and lung damage,

Ethylene
Ethylene is used as a plant hormone for ripening fruit. It is also used to produce polyethylene (a polymer of ethylene and the world's most widely used plastic) as well as ethylene glycol, which is the primary component of antifreeze. Ethylene has been used as an anaesthetic in the past, but is highly dangerous being an asphyxiate, combustible and a class-3 carcinogen.

Formaldehyde
Formaldehyde, although proven dangerous for the developing foetus in pregnant women in the past, is still commonly found in a variety of cleaning products, personal care products and even face tissues and toilet paper. It can also be found in grocery bags, fabrics, foam insulation, furniture, paper, plywood, soft furnishings, tobacco smoke, waxed paper and emissions from natural gas and kerosene cookers. It is also used in adhesive binders in floor coverings, carpet backing, fabric stiffeners and wrinkle-resistant materials, fire retardants, permanent pressed clothes and water repellents. Formaldehyde irritates the mucous membranes of the eyes, nose and throat and can cause asthma. It has also been linked with throat cancer in individuals that reside in mobile homes.

Nonane

Nonane is found in kerosene, paraffin wax candles and crayons, paint, petrol, printer ink, shoe soles, solvents, tobacco smoke and varnishes. It can cause asthma, confusion, depression, dizziness, euphoria, headache, inability to concentrate, liver and lung damage and taste dysfunction.

Ozone

Ozone is a colourless, unstable toxic gas with a pungent odour and powerful oxidising properties. It is the main component of air pollution, or smog, and is most often associated with outdoor air, but it also infiltrates indoor environments like homes and offices, and with people in industrialised countries spending as much of 80 to 90 percent of their time indoors, eliminating ozone is a health priority.

Ozone is best known with regard to the atmosphere's ozone layer. There are four atmospheres surrounding the earth:

1. The troposphere is the lowest region, extending from the earth's surface to a height of 0 to 16 km.
2. The stratosphere is from 16 to 50 km.
3. The mesosphere is from 50 to 80 km.
4. The thermosphere is from 80 to 640 km.

Ozone is a gas that is found in the stratosphere, where it protects life on earth by blocking the sun's ultraviolet (UV) waves and preventing them from reaching the earth's surface. However, it is also found in the troposphere, where it can damage living tissue and human-produced objects. It is generated from certain types of pollution and natural sources (hydrocarbons from plants and soil). Ozone can also be released by copy machines, laser printers, ultraviolet lights and some electrostatic air purification systems, all of which contribute to increased indoor ozone levels.

The extensive list of toxic effects of ozone on humans includes health conditions such as asthma, pulmonary oedema, haemorrhage, inflammation, reduction of lung function and sinus problems.

Paint

There are many volatile organic compounds (VOCs) in paint that will evaporate easily into the air at room temperature and often give a distinctive smell. (They are also emitted from many other sources, including fuels, numerous industrial operations and household products, such as cleaning agents, cosmetics and aerosols.) They can accelerate the rate nitrogen oxides (from combustion processes) react with sunlight to create low-level ozone and photochemical smog, which contributes to air pollution, and can add to the toxic overload in the human body.

Polychlorinated biphenyls (PCBs)

PCBs were used as coolants or lubricants in electrical equipment. They have been banned in many countries now due to the fact they do not break down easily and can attach to soil and sediment in water. PCBs build up in fish that eat the sediment and other animals that eat the fish, allowing an accumulation of PCBs that are thousands of time higher than what was in the water or soil. As they accumulate, they become more toxic.

Due to the way PCBs are structured, they are able to travel long distances in the air, polluting where PCBs were never used directly. They are also easily absorbed through skin and in the lungs. This increases the likelihood of animals and humans accumulating toxic amounts.

Exposure causes rashes and acne, as well as changes in blood and urine, indicating liver damage, and is associated with liver cancer and cancer of the biliary tract. Babies exposed to PCBs in the womb have lower birth weight and poorer memory and motor skills that have been shown to continue into the child's 11th year.

Radon

Radon gas escapes from the Earth's surface constantly and is considered harmless in open air, accounting for half of a person's exposure to radiation. A by-product of naturally-occurring radium and uranium breaking down, radon, is problematic only if it gets trapped in poorly ventilated homes, which can happen in areas where geological conditions produce it in higher concentrations.

The largest affected areas in the UK are the south-west of England, the Yorkshire Dales and Wales, but there are many other affected parts such as Lincoln, Milton Keynes, Nottingham, the Forest of Dean, the Peak District, much of Northern Ireland, the southern border of Scotland and Aberdeenshire. It is concentrated in parts of the country rich in granite such as Dartmoor, in Devon, and Cornwall.

The becquerel (symbol Bq) is the SI derived unit of radioactivity.

'SI' refers to the International System of Units. Bq/m3 is a unit of activity concentration, a measure of radon per unit volume. This can be thought of as the concentration of radon in the air, whether in a house, a school or outdoors. Values for activity concentration in Bq/m3 can range from about 3 (outdoors in the UK), through 50 (reported outdoors in some USA states), to 150,000 or more (found in the worst affected American and East German houses).

The average concentration of radon in UK housing is around 20 Bq/m3. The average for houses in Cornwall is around 170 and in Devon about 70 Bq/m3. This compares with an average of between 50 and 60 Bq/m3 in the USA. In general, radon levels in UK housing are low compared with many countries.

However, the radon concentration in a building does not represent the associated risk - the amount of time spent in the building is of equal importance. Ensuring there is adequate ventilation in the home (and underneath it in some cases) is imperative in areas with naturally high levels and there are free radon tests available. Using a wood burning stove can draw more radon into the home, especially if the covering of the ground is not sufficiently airtight.

Within affected counties in the UK there can be large areas that are substantially unaffected even within an area said to be at risk and this is because of variations in the underlying ground.

NOTE: Scammers have tried to use radon level scare tactics to lower house prices. Always have levels checked professionally.

Styrene

Styrene is found in bathtubs, boats, building insulation, cars, disposable cups, floor waxes and polishes, plastic packaging, personal care products, and rubber products such as shoes, tyres and conveyer belts. It is also approved for use in containers and food-contact materials and as a synthetic flavouring in ice cream and confectionary. In May 2013, the Washington DC District Court dismissed the styrene industry's challenge to the identification of styrene as 'reasonably anticipated to be a human carcinogen'. The US Environmental Protection Agency regulates styrene as a 'Hazardous Air Pollutant' and has described it as 'a suspected toxin to the gastrointestinal tract, kidneys and respiratory system among others'.

Tobacco smoke

Tobacco smoke contains many toxic chemicals on this list, including benzene and formaldehyde, plus other dangerous pollutants, such as nitrosamines, hydrogen cyanide and heavy metals. The smoke remains in the atmosphere of a room for many hours afterwards.

Toluene

Toluene is found in acrylic paints, adhesives, glue, lacquers, paint thinners, petrol, rubber cement, shoe polish, varnishes and waxes. It is highly lipophilic, meaning it readily crosses the blood-brain barrier, which accounts for its serious effects on the central nervous system. It reduces metabolic function in the brain, especially the hippocampus, pons and thalamus. The pons is a major structure in the upper part of the brain stem that is involved in the control of breathing, communication between different parts of the brain and sensations such as balance, hearing and taste.

Toluene can also cause asthma, ataxia, blindness, cardiac arrhythmia, confusion, decreased cognitive ability, delusions, dizziness, euphoria, hallucinations, headache, hearing loss, hypokalaemia, liver and kidney damage, lung damage, muscle weakness, nausea, optic and peripheral neuropathies, seizures, stupor, tinnitus, vertigo, vomiting, weak and brittle bones and coma.

Trichloroethylene
Trichloroethylene is found in clothes that have been dry-cleaned, glue, lacquers, paint, printing inks, varnishes and in the metal degreasing industry and has been linked with cancer of the liver.

VOCs (volatile organic compounds) see Paint (page 13)

Wax candles and beeswax polish
Some manufacturers bleach candles and beeswax using ionisation, sulphuric acid or hydrogen peroxide, which results in toxic compounds. If candles or beeswax have a medicinal odour, the chances are that the wax has been chemically altered or bleached and should be avoided. Reputable health-conscious suppliers of beeswax products can be found.

Xylene

Xylene is found in glue, lacquers, nail polish, plastic, petrol, rubber cement, solvents and varnishes. It causes a depression of the central nervous system leading to dizziness, headache, nausea and vomiting. It can also cause kidney and liver damage, loss of coordination, respiratory failure and even death.

The A to Z of studied houseplants

While all plants will clear carbon dioxide and very many probably have the capabilities of the plants described in this section, only those listed here have been studied for their toxin-removing abilities in sealed and ventilation-controlled atmospheres. We do know that the more plants there are in a room the more toxins will be removed as they all absorb particulates from the air at the same time as they take in carbon dioxide for photosynthesis.

Besides plants removing pollutants, the microorganisms associated with them in the potting soil also contribute to the cleaning effect. They can ingest pathogenic bacteria, viruses and pollutants and turn them into food for the plant. Plants are capable of removing many of the more than 300 chemicals found in the air of a spacecraft and studies have shown that houseplants are able to remove up to 87% of these airborne toxins in 24 hours and can also reduce house dust levels by 20%. Plants should be grown in soil which has activated carbon pellets added for more powerful results. These pellets should last about 12 to 18 months before new ones need to be added. It is possible to produce this air cleaning effect with as few as just a 5% space filled with plants in any size of room.

Aloe vera

Botanical name: *Aloe barbadensis*

Toxins cleared: Benzene and formaldehyde.

Aloe vera is a succulent that loves the sun and needs very little care and only a small amount of water. It must not stand in water and is best allowed to dry out completely between watering and is easy to grow on a sunny windowsill.

Aloe leaves contain a liquid gel which is full of amino acids, chlorophyll, enzymes, minerals, vitamins and other compounds that are responsible for its being called the 'plant of immortality' by the ancient Egyptians and 'the wand of heaven' by the native tribes of the Americas. They were aware of its powerful properties that assist the functions of the gastrointestinal tract and help the body to maintain healthy tissues both inside and out. Aloe vera's antibacterial, anti-inflammatory and wound-healing properties can be used to treat many different skin disorders, including sunburn and psoriasis. It is also a safe herbal medicine to use on animals.

The aloe vera plant will produce many baby shoots within just a year that can be re-potted into new plants.

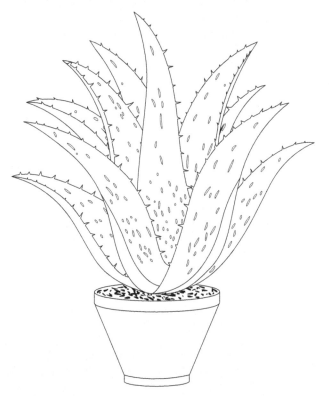

Areca palm

Botanical name: *Chrysalidocarpus lutescens*

Toxins cleared: Benzene, formaldehyde and trichloroethylene amongst many others.

The areca palm is native to Madagascar and can reach a height of 6-8 feet inside but outdoors it may grow as tall as 25 feet. Its nickname, 'the butterfly palm', comes from its long feathery fronds (leaves) arching upwards from multiple reed-like stems. These palms require bright, indirect light. Too much light or direct sun burns the fronds and causes them to turn yellow.

Allow the top 2.5 to 5 cm (one to two inches) of soil to dry out before watering and never allow the plant to sit in water as this causes root rot. The fronds of an areca wilt when they need water but quickly perk up once the soil is soaked. Like all palms, Arecas do not like chemicals or salt, so avoid water that has passed through a softener or contains fluoride or chlorine as this causes freckle-like spots on the leaves.

Feed an areca palm monthly when it is actively growing with a balanced liquid fertiliser at half the recommended strength and, as it requires high humidity, spray lightly with water often. It thrives well in temperatures between 18 and 24°C (65 and 75°F) during the day and around 12°C (55°F) at night. It can be placed outside during the summer but must be brought in at night if temperatures go below 10°C (50°F).

Azalea

Botanical name: *Rhododendron simsii*

Toxin cleared: Formaldehyde.

Azaleas are related to rhododendrons and blueberries and are part of an ancient group of plants dating back millions of years. They are also the national flower of Nepal. They thrive in temperatures between 15 and 18°C (60 and 65°F). They need to be watered regularly and, as they also absorb water through their foliage, it is a good idea to mist the leaves with water regularly from a spray bottle too.

NOTE: The azalea plant contains grayanotoxins which, if eaten, can lead to vomiting, seizures and cardiac arrest in all animal species. These plants are considered very poisonous and should be kept away from pets and children.

Bamboo palm

Botanical name: *Chamaedorea sefritzii*

Toxins cleared: Benzene, formaldehyde and trichloroethylene.

The bamboo palm is native to Mexico and Central America and thrives in low-light areas. Indoors, it can reach a height of 120 cm to 365 cm (4 to 12 ft) and a width of 90 to 152 cm (3 to 5 ft) with multiple reed-like stems growing in clumps.

The bamboo palm thrives in full sun or bright light and shady areas and filters large quantities of air if allowed to reach its full height.

Banana fig

Botanical name: *Ficus maeleilandii alii, Ficus macleilandii*

Toxins cleared: A variety of toxins including formaldehyde.

The banana fig is happy in full sun or partial shade and thrives in a temperature range of 13 to 24°C (55 to75°F), although exposure to lower temperatures above 7°C (45°F) is tolerated for short periods of time. Provide filtered sunlight or bright indirect light but avoid direct sunlight from hot windows, which may scorch the plant. If it is situated against a wall, it is best to rotate the plant every few days to prevent the back of the plant from losing its leaves.

Allow the top centimetre (0.4 inch) of potting mixture to dry out between watering. Use tepid water, as cold water may cause leaf loss. Do not allow the plant to stand in water and never allow the potting mixture to dry out. During the active growth period (spring and summer), feed once every two weeks with standard liquid fertiliser. Decrease fertiliser gradually in autumn and refrain from feeding completely during the winter. Mist often as the banana fig prefers high humidity.

NOTE: Hand protection should be used whilst dealing with this house plant for those who have allergic reactions to latex.

Banana tree

Botanical name: *Muso Oriana*

Toxin cleared: Formaldehyde

The banana plant needs rich, humus-like and well-draining soil as well as plenty of filtered sunlight through windows to prevent leaf scorching. They need humid conditions and very warm temperatures to thrive; night temperatures around 19°C (67°F) are ideal and day temperatures of 26°C (80°F). Water sparingly during the rest period in autumn and winter; give plenty of water and feed fortnightly during the spring and summer growth period.

Boston fern

Botanical name: *Nephrolepis exaltata bostoniensis*

Toxins cleared: Arsenic, formaldehyde and mercury.

These plants prefer to clean the air from a cool location with high humidity and indirect light. They are relatively easy to grow, but they do need to stay moist. Check soil daily, to see if it needs water, and give it a good soak once per month. If fern leaf tips are turning brown because of low humidity, try standing the plant on a wet pebble tray. Be sure it is sitting on the pebbles and not in the water.

The Boston fern does very well in hanging baskets but, as it needs plenty of humidity, would suit a bathroom best. Boston ferns prefer cool temperatures between 15 and 21°C (60 and 70°F). Keep all types of ferns away from heat sources such as fireplaces.

Chinese evergreen

Botanical name: *Aglaonema crispum 'Deborah'*

Toxins cleared: Many air pollutants and toxins.

The Chinese evergreen is very easy to care for and only needs low light. It emits more oxygen than most other plants and is listed by NASA as one of the top 10 toxin-removing plants. During the active growth period water moderately, making the potting mixture moist, but allowing the top 2-3 cm (0.78-1 inch) of the mixture to dry between watering. During the rest period (which may be very short or even non-existent) water only enough to keep the potting moisture from drying out completely.

High humidity is required by the Chinese evergreen, so standing the plant on a tray of wet pebbles and misting the leaves regularly can help it thrive. Use liquid feed monthly except during the rest period.

NOTE: This plant is poisonous and should not be kept within reach of young children and pets.

Chrysanthemum

Botanical name: *Chrysantheium morifolium*

Toxins cleared: Ammonia, benzene, formaldehyde and xylene.

Chrysanthemums were brought to Japan [from where?] by Buddhist monks in 400 AD and have remained a very important part of Japanese culture to this day. The flowers last three to four weeks indoors with very little care and in almost any environment before needing to be replaced. The chrysanthemum is rated, by NASA, as one of the best pollutant removers of them all.

It prefers direct sunlight which will help the plant open its buds. Dead head to gain more flowers.

NOTE: All parts of this popular flowering plant are potentially toxic to dogs, cats, horses and other mammals. Ingesting the plant can cause vomiting, diarrhoea, excessive salivating, rashes and a lack of coordination.

Corn cane

Botanical name: *Dracaena massangeana*

Toxin cleared: Formaldehyde.

The corn cane is a member of the ginger family and is also known as the ornamental ginger, marble ginger, striped narrow leaf ginger, Sander's ginger and variegate ginger. It is native to a region in the Bismarck Archipelago in the Solomon Islands. It only needs low water and low light so it does very well in many areas of the home. However, it does need high humidity so standing it on a tray of wet pebbles and misting the leaves regularly can help it thrive. While it can live in low light, it prefers medium light or filtered sunlight. If it is kept in too dark a position leaf variegation will be reduced and prolonged direct sunlight can cause foliage to scald, brown or bleach.

During the warm season the corn cane can be moved outdoors to a position with partial shade but must be brought back inside before the temperature drops below 15°C (59°F). As soon as the rhizomes start to grow in early spring, begin to water plentifully to keep the potting mixture thoroughly moist. After the active growth period gradually reduce the quantity and water only moderately during the rest period. Apply a liquid feed every two weeks from spring to summer. Remove leaves when they are dying off and cut old canes to their base.

NOTE: All members of the *Dracaena* family are toxic to dogs and cats.

Devil's ivy or Golden pothos

Botanical name: *Scindapsus aures*

Toxins cleared: Formaldehyde and other volatile compounds.

The native range of Devil's ivy extends from Northern Australia through Malaysia and Indochina into China, Japan and India. It grows very fast and can flourish in dark areas of the home. Water it regularly but less so in cold weather. Leaf drop is a good indication of over watering; however, the leaves do need frequent misting as the plant requires high humidity. In warm rooms it is advisable to stand pots on trays of wet pebbles and suspend saucers of water under hanging baskets. Apply liquid feed about once every two weeks during the active growth period in the spring and summer but wait six months before feeding new plants.

NOTE: Both the stem and the leaves of this common houseplant contain insoluble calcium oxalates. Chewing or biting into the plant releases the crystals which penetrate tissue, resulting in injury. These steroidal saponins and glycosides cause tissue irritation and possible swelling when chewed and lead to oral irritation, intense burning and irritation of the mouth, tongue and lips, excessive drooling and foaming at the mouth, difficulty breathing and swallowing, loss of appetite and vomiting.

Dragon tree

Botanical name: *Dracaena marginata*

Toxins cleared: Benzene, formaldehyde, trichloroethylene and xylene.

Bright conditions with some shade are suitable for the dragon plant as direct sunlight will damage the leaves. It grows very tall and it is natural if the leaves start dying and coming away at the bottom of the plant, similar to the way in which a yucca tree sheds its bottom leaves for new growth. They can be removed when they start deteriorating in looks.

Allow dracaenas to dry slightly between watering. Wait until the soil surface is dry to the touch, then soak thoroughly with tepid (not cold) water.

NOTE: The dragon tree is toxic to animals such as cats and dogs if eaten.

Dwarf pygmy date palm

Botanical name: *Phoenix roebelenii*

Toxins cleared: Formaldehyde and xylene.

The dwarf palm thrives in filtered light but can also withstand bright full sunlight. Water sparingly, making the potting compost barely moist during the rest period. When active growth begins in the spring, increase the amount of water given gradually and keep the potting compost thoroughly moist during the growing season but never allow pots to stand in water. Only use warm water and as winter approaches, begin to reduce amounts gradually once more.

Apply a liquid feed to established plants once every two weeks during the active growth period only.

The dwarf pygmy palm grows well in normal room temperatures, but thrives better if kept at about 10 to13°C (50 to 55°F) during the winter rest period.

NOTE: This palm has sharp needle-like spines arranged near the base of the leaf stem. These can easily penetrate skin and may result in painful infections. Due to this, always keep out of the reach of young children.

English ivy

Botanical name: *Hedera helix*

Toxins cleared: Airborne particles of faecal-matter such as methane, benzene and formaldehyde. Said to help reduce asthma and allergies.

English ivy is an invasive plant species native to most of Europe and western Asia. It thrives in bright filtered to low light. Ample light helps the leaves become more colourful, but filtering it prevents drying, leaf loss and poor growth. Fluctuating temperatures can cause problems; always keep it away from drafts. In temperatures above 18°C (64°F), provide extra humidity by standing the pot on a dish of wet pebbles. Water freely during summer growth and keep the soil moist in the winter. Spraying with water weekly in the summer will help prevent spider mite infestation. Feed once a month with liquid feed diluted to a quarter of normal strength.

NOTE: English ivy contains serious toxins. The cell sap can cause redness, itching and/or blisters on the skin. Symptoms of ingestion include an immediate burning sensation in the throat and mouth, possibly followed by redness, blisters, rash and obvious visible irritation of the lining of the mouth; excessive drooling, obvious pain or discomfort of the mouth, (in animals) pawing at the mouth, hoarse or weak vocalisation; excessive thirst and gastrointestinal upset such as abdominal pain, diarrhoea and vomiting.

Gerbera or Barberton daisy

Botanical name: *Gerbera jamesonii*

Toxins cleared: Formaldehyde and xylene, and clears benzene and trichloroethylene more exceptionally than other plants.

The gerbera daisy thrives in full sun so is ideal for a bright windowsill, where it will get some direct sunlight; however, it will need some afternoon shade in hot summer climates. Growing it on a patio is another option, as long as the temperature doesn't rise above 24°C (75°F). The daisy thrives in cool to average temperatures of 13 to 24°C (55 to 75°F). Bring plants indoors when the weather begins to cool in the autumn, and they will live for several years, even blooming in the winter.

They need moderate watering as rot will occur if the crowns are buried or the drainage is poor. The soil should always be moist, but never wet, and they must never stand in water. Always wait until the top 2-3 cm (one inch) of soil is dry before watering again.

They require fortnightly feeding with a weak liquid feed, especially in summer, to promote flowering. Deadheading will encourage a longer blooming season and removing old leaves promptly helps prevent fungus from growing on the plant.

49

Heart leaf or Sweet heart plant

Botanical name: *Philodendron hederaceum* is the correct name but it is sometimes called *Philodendron cordatum*, *Philodendron cuspidatum*, *Philodendron micans*, *Philodendron oxycardium* or *Philodendron scandens*

Toxins cleared: Formaldehyde and many other air pollutants; capable of absorbing between 80% and 90% of the formaldehyde present in water-based paint, roofing felt or insulation material, glues in fitted carpets and laminated wood floors.

Also known as the 'sweetheart plant', this philodendron is a vine with aerial roots native to Central America and the Caribbean. Many philodendrons have two growth phases – a juvenile form and a mature form – which often look very different in leaf size and shape. Container-grown plants usually stay in the juvenile phase. They can withstand many climates, grow very rapidly and can be made to climb anywhere, thriving in low light, but cannot tolerate temperatures below 13°C (55°F). Pinch out growing tips from time to time to provide a bushier shape as otherwise they can become spindly. When watering, soak the entire surface of the soil, then leave until around 50% is dry before watering again. When the plant is producing new leaves, provide liquid feed at 50% the normal dose every fortnight. Mist with purified water to increase the humidity and hence leaf size. Toxic if eaten.

Holy basil

Botanical name: *Ocimum tenuiflorum*

Toxins cleared: Carbon dioxide and carbon monoxide.

Holy basil is one of the few plants that emit oxygen 20 hours a day and it also absorbs many types of harmful gases. It is a tropical plant that needs high humidity and dislikes direct sunlight. It requires plenty of moisture in the soil, needing to be watered at least three times daily in summer and at least once a day in winter. It requires a liquid feed only once a month at half strength during the summer.

It is a herb with powerful antibacterial and medicinal properties similar to, but more potent than, the common basil plant. Substances in the leaves are a nerve tonic and also sharpen memory and promote the removal of catarrh and phlegm and induce copious perspiration. In cases of acute fever, a decoction of the leaves boiled with powdered cardamom in half a litre of water and mixed with honey and milk can bring down the temperature. The seeds of the plant are mucilaginous (produce gel) once exposed to water, like chia and flaxseeds, and this is good for digestive health. Holy basil is thought also to relieve stress, improve energy levels and endurance, support healthy immune function and promote healthy gastric tissue. It also benefits the heart as a blood thinner, promotes good circulation and when taken daily, can lower high blood pressure by helping optimise cholesterol levels.

Kimberly queen fern

Botanical name: *Nephrolepis obliterate*

Toxins cleared: Formaldehyde, toluene and xylene.

The Kimberly queen fern, or Australian sword fern as it is also known, is more compact and easier to care for than most other ferns and makes an ideal hanging plant. It prefers light but not direct sunshine. Always allow the top 5-7 cm (two to three inches) of soil to dry out before watering; crispy brown leaves in the centre of the plant are an indication of overwatering. Feed once a month in the spring and summer and every other month in autumn and winter with a diluted liquid plant food at half the recommended strength. The fern needs high humidity so stand the pot on a tray or saucer filled with pebbles and water, but not in the water.

Lady palm

Botanical name: *Rhapis excelsa*

Toxins cleared: A general air purifier, especially of benzene, and formaldehyde, toluene, trichloroethylene and xylene.

The lady palm thrives well when slightly root-bound, so it should be kept it in a smallish pot. In a 25 cm (10 inch) or larger pot, it can grow up to 4.27 cm (14 feet) tall. It prefers indirect light and evenly moist, but not soggy, soil during the growing season. Like many palms, it is sensitive to boron, chlorine and fluoride, so it is best to allow tap water to stand for 24-48 hours before using it or use distilled water instead. The foliage should be misted daily or stand the pot on a tray or saucer of wet pebbles. Brown leaf tips are caused by irregular watering and dry air but may be snipped off with scissors.

If allowed to get too dry lady palm can get infected by red spider mite so it is best to also wipe the leaves with a damp cloth now and then.

Lily turf

Botanical name: Liriope spicata

Toxin cleared: Ammonia and formaldehyde.

Lily turf can grow in filtered sunlight or partial or full shade and is evergreen so makes an ideal house plant. It requires watering when the top 5 cm (2 in) of soil has dried out and feeding once a month from early summer to help produce more flowers in the summer and autumn, but not during the winter.

It thrives in humid conditions so is best kept in a bathroom or on a tray or dish of wet pebbles.

Mother-in-law's tongue or Snake plant

Botanical name: Sansevieria trifasciata Laurentii

Toxin cleared: 107 toxins including formaldehyde, nicotine, nitrogen oxide, toluene and xylene.

The mother-in-law's tongue is native to India, Indonesia and Africa and is one of the hardiest and easiest houseplants to grow. It is also one of the plants that releases oxygen at night instead of carbon dioxide so is a useful plant for the bedroom. It can thrive in low light conditions (60-80% shade) and is very drought tolerant and, although it does need to be watered occasionally, it generally prefers drier conditions.

Let the soil dry between watering and, during winter, reduce watering to monthly or whenever the soil is dry to the touch. Water every other week during the growing season and only the soil as water on the leaves will cause them to rot. Never allow the pot to stand in water either.

Feed with a mild cactus feed during the growing season (spring and summer) and do not feed in the autumn or winter.

NOTE: Mother-in-law's tongue is toxic if eaten so is not recommended in children's bedrooms or where pets can reach it.

Moth orchid

Botanical name: Phalaenopsis amabilis

Toxin cleared: Formaldehyde.

The moth orchid is native to Australia, Indonesia and the surrounding islands and not only absorbs carbon dioxide, but also releases oxygen at night, making it suitable for bedrooms. It loves sunshine (but not midday sun) and lots of water, best added in the morning, once the top centimetre (0.4 inch) or so of the potting mixture has dried out. Do not water in the middle of the leaves as this can lead to them rotting, and do not allow the plant to stand in water. Never let any beads of moisture stay on the leaves as this can cause rot and fungus infections and black spots will appear if the moisture remains on them for just one single night. Use an orchid liquid fertiliser every two weeks or a foliar feed with every third or fourth watering.

A minimum temperature of 20°C (68°F) throughout the year is essential, along with high humidity; therefore, plants thrive best if stood on trays of moist pebbles or are lightly misted with water early in the morning. They will naturally shed leaves after some time and every two years plants should be moved into slightly larger containers using a peat or bark based mixture. They thrive especially well in wire or wooden baskets lined with sphagnum moss.

Peace lily

Botanical name: Spathiphyllum wallisii

Toxins cleared: Benzene, formaldehyde, toluene, trichloroethylene and xylene.

The peace lily is found growing wild in tropical rain forest regions of Central America, usually in wet habitats with low light. It has major air-cleaning abilities and is easy to grow. It will flower for much of the summer which produces some pollen and floral scents so those with allergies may wish to avoid it.

Grow peace lilies in a shady spot as direct sunlight may burn the leaves; however, if light is too low they may not produce many flowers. Allow the top centimetre (0.4 inch) or so of the potting mixture to dry out before watering and if temperatures fall below 15°C (59°F) for more than a day or two, reduce the quantity of water, making the potting mixture barely moist; however, it is important not to allow the potting mixture to dry out completely. Apply a liquid feed every two weeks from early spring to late autumn when growth is most active, but continue feeding throughout the year if the plant is actively growing in a peat-based mixture. When flowers start to fade, cut off their stalks as close to the base as possible. Re-pot into one size larger every spring until the size is as desired; then, every five years, the plant will need dividing as it will become pot bound and suffer as a result.

NOTE: Ingestion can cause irritation of the tongue and lips, increased salivation, difficulty swallowing and vomiting in most mammals.

Rubber plant

Botanical name: Ficus elastica, Ficus robusta, Peperomia obtusifolia

Toxins cleared: Clears a variety of toxins including formaldehyde.

The rubber plant is native to India and Malaysia and was once grown for the rubber that was produced from its sap, hence the name. It does not like to be moved around and it needs rich soil, filtered light but does not need watering often. Allow the top of the soil to dry out and water sparingly during cooler months. Both overwatering and underwatering will turn the leaves yellow and, in some species, overwatering will cause the leaves to fall off. Only add a diluted liquid feed sparingly once a month during the active growing season (spring and summer).

Always place rubber plants away from air-conditioners, drafts, fires and heaters as they require constant temperatures. If placed in a dark area they will produce weak stems and small leaves. They emit especially high levels of oxygen.

NOTE: All parts of the rubber plant are poisonous to pets if ingested.

Spider plant

Botanical name: *Chlorophytum comosum*

Toxins cleared: Benzene, carbon monoxide, formaldehyde and xylene.

The spider plant is very hardy and easy to grow and prefers bright but indirect sunlight. Allow the top 50% of the soil to dry out before watering. The green of a spider plant's leaves will begin to fade when it requires water and become green again once it has been watered. Brown tips can be caused by using water that is high in salts and chemicals. Only use a liquid feed sparingly once a month at half strength during the summer. Too much feed will also make the leaf tips turn brown.

The spider plant will throw out flowering shoots which turn into baby spider plants that can be potted up to give away to friends. It is a good plant to keep in a hanging basket.

NOTE: The spider plant is non-toxic so therefore a good choice to have around children or pets.

Umbrella tree

Botanical name: *Brassaia actinophylla*

Toxin cleared: Benzene.

The umbrella tree, also known as Amate, octopus tree, Queensland umbrella tree or *Schefflera actinophylla*, prefers plenty of water and humidity but only needs indirect sunshine to thrive and can survive in shady areas. It needs plenty of water during the summer, once or twice a week, and the leaves should be misted occasionally. During the winter, water once a week and mist every two weeks. Never allow it to stand in water as this will cause the leaves to become yellow and wither. It will thrive well if the leaves are cleaned regularly with a damp sponge.

Feed once a month during the summer season with a diluted liquid feed. It may grow long spindly stems if the temperature is too warm and there is not enough light and it may need to be supported by canes when it reaches a certain height. Pinching out the top growing tips can make it become bushier.

NOTE: It is toxic to cats and dogs. Chewing or biting into this plant releases insoluble calcium oxalate crystals which penetrate tissue resulting in injury. Clinical signs may be seen immediately and include pawing at the face (secondary to oral pain), drooling, foaming and vomiting. Moderate to severe swelling of the lips, tongue, oral cavity and upper airway may also be seen, making it difficult to breathe or swallow.

Warneck dracaena

Botanical name: Dracaena deremensis, Dracaena fragrans

Toxins cleared: Benzene and trichloroethylene.

The Warneck dracaena, also known as the corn plant, Chinese money tree and the happy plant, is native to tropical Africa. It does not need direct sunlight so is the perfect indoor plant and can grow to around 12 feet tall. It requires fluoride-free water and does not enjoy saturated roots. Water regularly once or twice a week during the summer to keep the soil moist but sparingly during the winter. Brown leaf tips can be the result of allowing the potting soil to dry out too much.

It needs high humidity so mist regularly with fluoride-free water. Use a half strength liquid feed once a month during the growing season. It can become deficient in iron and this can show as yellowing of the leaves between the veins. Use a seaweed-based feed if this occurs. The leaves may also show damage if the temperature drops below 10°C (50°F).

NOTE: The warneck plant is toxic to animals such as cats and dogs if eaten.

Wax begonia

Botanical name: *Begonia semperflorens*

Toxins cleared: Benzene and toluene.

The wax begonia originated in Mexico and needs plenty of indirect light. It flowers during the summer. It does not tolerate temperatures below 10°C (50°F) and will suffer in dry air. Stand the pot on moist pebbles to increase humidity but do not allow it to stand in water and avoid wetting the leaves.

Add a liquid feed every couple of weeks when the plant is actively growing. Overwatering and poor air circulation can result in brown and black spots on the leaves. Always allow the top of the soil to dry out before watering again.

NOTE: All species of begonia are toxic to pets.

Weeping fig

Botanical name: *Ficus benjamina*

Toxins cleared: Good general air purifier, especially against benzene, formaldehyde and trichloroethylene.

The weeping fig should be placed in bright, but indirect sunlight and the top 25% of the soil should be allowed to dry out between watering. Underwatering will cause the leaves to turn yellow and overwatering will cause them to fall off. Reduce watering significantly during the winter months. Feed sparingly once a month using a liquid feed at half the strength during the spring and summer months and none during the winter.

Any fluctuation in light, temperature or water can cause many leaves to fall off the *Ficus benjamina* plant but there are new hybrids that do not do this such as *Ficus alli, Ficus amstel, Ficus midnight, Ficus Monique* and *Ficus wintergreen*. Direct sun will burn the leaves of all species of weeping figs and air conditioners, drafts and heaters can also cause leaf drop.

NOTE: All parts of the weeping fig tree are poisonous to pets if ingested and those with an allergy to latex may have issues with this plant.

> **GENERAL NOTE:** Many other plants are also capable of removing toxins but have not yet been studied fully.

Summary – which plants are best for which problems

General cleansers
- Wide variety – areca palm, banana fig, Chinese evergreen, rubber plant
- Air pollutants – heart leaf plant, weeping fig
- Harmful gases (CO_2, CO) – holy basil, spider plant

Specific cleansers
- airborne faecal material – English ivy
- ammonia - chrysanthemum
- arsenic – Boston fern
- benzene – aloe vera, chrysanthemum, dragon tree, gerbera (particularly effective), lady palm, peace lily, spider plant, umbrella tree, warneck dracaena, wax begonia, weeping fig
- formaldehyde – ale vera, azalea, bamboo palm, banana fig, banana tree, Boston fern, chrysanthemum, corn cane, devil's ivy, dragon tree, dwarf pygmy date palm, gerbera, heart leaf

plant, Kimberly queen fern, lady palm, lily turf, mother in law's tongue, snake plant, moth orchid, peace lily, rubber plant, spider plant, weeping fig

- mercury – Boston fern
- methane – English ivy
- toluene – Kimberly queen fern, peace lily, wax begonia
- trichloroethylene – bamboo palm, dragon tree, gerbera (particularly effective), lady palm, peace lily, warneck dracaena, weeping fig
- VOCs – devil's ivy
- xylene – chrysanthemum, dragon tree, dwarf pygmy date palm, gerbera, Kimberly queen fern, lady palm, peace lily, spider plant.

Plants toxic to animals and young children

In addition to those noted in the A to Z, there are some other house plants that are particularly toxic to small children and pets:

Amaryllis (Amaryllis belladonna, Amaryllis paradisicola)
Ingestion of the many toxins in this popular flowering houseplant, such as amaryllidine, haemanthamine, hippeastrine, hydroxyvittatine, lycorine, pancracine, tazzetine, vittatine and others, can lead to abdominal pain, accelerated defaecation, anorexia, dark brown urine, diarrhoea, excessive drooling, gastroenteritis, lethargy, shivering, vomiting and possible contact dermatitis in the mouth, throat and nose and on the face. Ingestion of larger amounts can cause paralysis, central nervous system collapse and death.

Angel's trumpets (Brugmansia)
This plant has large, fragrant flowers that give them their common name of angel's trumpets. All parts are poisonous to pets and humans as they are part of the nightshade family.

Autumn crocus (Colchicum autumnale)

The autumn crocus contains compounds that rapidly attack dividing cells in the body. Ingestion by animals can cause vomiting, diarrhoea and possible death. (It should not be confused with the spring flowering crocuses such as *Crocus chrysanthus*, *Crocus speciosus* or *Crocus vernus* as these are not toxic.)

Avocado (Persea Americana)

Avocado plants are toxic to cats and dogs and can cause diarrhoea and vomiting.

Bay leaves or laurels (Laurus nobilis)

Bay leaves contain grayanotoxins which can lead to vomiting, seizures and cardiac arrest in all animal species.

Cannabis (Cannabis sativa)

Ingestion of both the plant or the smoke from burning it are toxic to animals and can cause paranoia leading to agitation, anxiety and panting in pets. They may also lose the ability to consume food and water and become dehydrated, which can lead to kidney disorders.

Extreme responses to noises, movements and other forms of sensory stimulation may occur in pets that are exposed to cannabis. These responses can manifest as trembling or jerking of the head or extremities. In severe cases, the responses may appear similar to seizures.

Castor bean (Ricinus Communis)

Castor beans contain ricin which, even in very small doses, can cause multiple organ failure. It is most highly concentrated in the seeds but the seed coating must be damaged to release this toxin therefore, if seeds are swallowed whole, they may pass through the digestive system and not do any harm. However, these beans are commonly used to make ornaments and jewellery which could get chewed and swallowed by children or animals.

Chives, garlic, leeks and onions (Allium)

All plants from the *Allium* family can cause anaemia and gastrointestinal disorders in cats and dogs.

Cyclamen (Cyclamen persicum)

The cyclamen is a common houseplant that contains irritating saponins and, when any part of the plant (especially the tubers or roots) are chewed or ingested by dogs and cats, it can result in drooling, vomiting and diarrhoea. With large ingestions, these plants can result in cardiac problems (e.g. abnormal heart rate and rhythm), seizures and death.

Daffodils, hyacinths and tulips (Narcissus, Hyacinthus, Tulipa)

When the plant parts or bulbs are chewed or ingested, it can result in tissue irritation in the mouth and oesophagus. Typical signs include profuse drooling, vomiting, and diarrhoea, depending on the amount consumed. With large ingestions, more severe symptoms, such as an increase in heart rate, changes in respiration and difficulty breathing, may be seen.

Foxgloves (Digitalis purpurae)
Foxgloves contain glycosides which slow down the heart beat and can even stop it and are toxic to all animals.

Hops (Humulus lupulis)
Hops are used in beer brewing and, if ingested, can cause a dog's body temperature to rise rapidly to as much as 42°C (108°F) and kill it. Signs are agitation and panting and can be seen within hours of ingestion. Allowing animals to consume beer is best avoided.

Japanese andromeda (Pieris japonica)
This plant is a member of the heather family and contains grayanotoxins which can lead to vomiting, seizures and cardiac arrest in all animal species.

Japanese yew (Taxus cuspidate)
This is an evergreen plant that contains compounds that have a direct action upon the heart. Ingestion of any part of the plant (except the fruits) can cause irregular heart beat and even stop the heart, causing death within a few hours of ingestion by any animal species.

Jimson weed or devil's trumpet (Datura stramonium)
Consumption of the jimson weed plant can cause restlessness,

drunken-like walking and respiratory failure in cats and dogs.

Kalanchoe (Bryophyllum pinnatum, Kalanchoe pinnatum)
The flowering kalanchoe is a popular houseplant that is a cousin to the jade plant and contains glycosides which slow down the heart beat and can even stop it and be fatal to all animals.

Lilies (Lilium)
Most species of lilies, especially Asiatic, day, Easter, Japanese and tiger varieties, can cause kidney failure in cats.

Lily of the valley (Convallaria majalis)
The lily of the valley plant contains glycosides which slow down the heart beat and can even stop it, and can be fatal to all animals.

Oleander (Nerium oleander)
Oleander is a popular houseplant that contains glycosides which slow down the heart beat and can even stop it, and can be fatal to all animals.

Rhubarb (Rheum rhabarbarum)
Rhubarb, and especially the leaves, can cause tremors and kidney failure in cats and dogs due to the soluble oxalate salts which are absorbed from the gastrointestinal tract and then bind with body's calcium, resulting in a sudden drop in calcium levels. Rarely, acute renal failure can be seen from ingestion of plants or fruit containing these soluble oxalate crystals. Clinical signs of this type of poisoning

include drooling, lack of appetite, vomiting, diarrhoea, lethargy, weakness, tremors, bloody urine and changes in thirst and urination in cats and dogs.

Sago palm plant (Cycas revolute)
The sago plant can cause diarrhoea, vomiting and seizures in cats and dogs, and liver failure in dogs.

Shamrock (Oxalis triangularis)
Shamrock, also known as sorrel, contains soluble oxalate salts which are absorbed from the gastrointestinal tract and then bind with body's calcium, resulting in a sudden drop in calcium levels. Rarely, acute renal failure can be seen from ingestion of plants or fruit containing these soluble oxalate crystals. Clinical signs of this type of poisoning include drooling, lack of appetite, vomiting, diarrhoea, lethargy, weakness, tremors, bloody urine and changes in thirst and urination in cats and dogs. Fortunately, shamrock tastes bitter so is rarely consumed in quantities large enough to cause any serious damage.

A note about fungus gnats

When potted plants are brought inside the home, they may also bring in the larvae of fungus gnats in the soil. The larvae feed on plant roots and fungi, helping in the decomposition of organic matter. The fungus gnats are very small, short-lived, flying insects and, after mating, the females look for places that are warm and moist to lay their eggs.

Some types of potting compost, even well-known brands, can be full of these larvae. Changing to another brand that is free of these larvae is one solution.

One way to reduce their numbers is to allow plants to dry out fully for a few days as this will kill off the larvae. However, this can be harmful to some plants.

A small dish of apple cider vinegar or red wine, placed near to plants, will attract and drown the gnats.

Adding sand on top of the compost can stop egg laying and gnats from coming out of the soil but this will water log the plant and may cause damage unless the sand is removed again after a week or so.

The gnats can try to fly in the nose and mouth as these may seem places they could lay eggs. However, this will not happen and they are harmless to plants, animals and humans and are more of an annoyance than a problem.

They are often mistaken for fruit flies.

Other benefits of growing plants in the home

Growing plants in the home can be very beneficial to the health not only because they remove airborne contaminants from the environment but also because some are nutritious herbs for both medicinal and catering use. Many also have volatile oils which can be used to clean both the home and the body without the use of the toxic chemicals found in most household cleaners that add to the burden of toxins already in the home. This is especially important when there are children, elderly and frail persons living in the household.

NOTE: The volatile oils in herbs should not be used by pregnant women.

Natural air fresheners

Spray aerosol air fresheners are highly inflammable and can cause irritation to the eyes and skin and trigger asthma attacks. Rather than use chemically-produced air fresheners, especially when infants or young children, the elderly, infirm patients or allergy sufferers are present, it is very simple to make natural versions. Of course an oil burner using essential oils is the easiest way to eliminate odours, including tobacco and pets, but the following are safer and cleaner alternatives.

Freshen the whole home
Ingredients

- Almond extract
- Basil
- Bergamot
- Cinnamon sticks
- Cloves
- Coconut extract
- Coriander
- Dill
- Eucalyptus
- Fennel
- Frankincense
- Ginger slices
- Jasmine
- Lemon balm
- Lemon slices
- Lemon grass
- Lavender
- Lime slices
- Mint
- Nutmeg
- Orange slices
- Oregano
- Peppermint
- Pineapple slices
- Pine needles
- Rosemary
- Rose petals
- Sage
- Sandalwood
- Savoury
- Spearmint
- Thyme
- Vanilla pods

Any other aromatic herbs and spices of choice can also be used.

Method

- Place a selection from the list (cut the fruits and ginger into slices) into a large jar, then fill with water.
- Screw on the lid, then place in the refrigerator overnight.
- The next day, pour the jar contents into a large pan and simmer on low to fill the house with the herbal and/or spicy aroma of choice.

Air freshener spray
Ingredients and equipment

- One clean spray bottle
- One tablespoon of bicarbonate of soda
- 500 ml distilled water
- Essential oils of choice (10 drops)

Method

Using a fork, mix the bicarbonate of soda and essential oil in a bowl. Pour the mixture in the bottle and fill it with distilled water. Shake the bottle before every use.

NOTE: Essential oils should not be used by pregnant women.

Natural home-made cleaners

Using more than one of the following aromatic herbs together not only provides natural antibacterial, antifungal and antiviral cleaning power, but also gives a choice of fragrances to mix and match. The fragrance that is preferred by an individual is going to provide them with an environment they feel psychologically more comfortable and relaxed in. Ask those who spend most of their time in a particular room for their own choice of herb.

Many of these herbs can be grown in pots on a sunny windowsill for use all year round and will also purify the air at the same time, which reduces the chemicals that fill our homes (see page 8). They can also be used diluted as natural body and facial washes and shampoos, reducing the toxic overload even further.

Aloe vera (Aloe barbadensis)

The sticky juice inside the aloe vera plant's leaves has powerful antibacterial properties and can be drunk as a juice for an internal cleanser and used on the skin for various skin conditions as well as being the ideal cleaner for all surfaces in the home. Chop one aloe vera leaf into small pieces and place in a mug. Pour boiled, hot (but not boiling) water over them and leave to steep for 15 minutes. Then strain and pour into a spray bottle.

Anise seeds (Pimpinella anisum)

Fragrant antibacterial action of the anise seed can provide a pleasant aroma as it cleans. Add a cup of boiled (but not boiling) water to three teaspoons of crushed seeds, steeping for 20 minutes.

Basil (Ocimum basilicum)

Basil kills *E. coli*, *Listeria* and *Salmonella* bacteria. Steep a handful of basil leaves in boiled water until it turns cold then strain the leaves and add the liquid to a spray bottle to disinfect surfaces. Basil grown in a pot indoors needs humidity and the soil needs to be kept moist.

Bay leaf (Laurus nobilis, Cinnamomum tamala)
Bay leaves are excellent as an antibacterial cleaner and can be used as a shampoo to clear dandruff. Steep them in very hot water for 20 minutes before straining.

Bergamot (Monarda didyma)
A species of bergamot called *Citrus bergamia* contains the antiseptic thymol.

Blue vervain (Verbena hastata, Verbena azul)
Blue vervain has properties that kill viruses.

Borage (Borago oficinalis)
Easily grown in the UK garden, borage leaves and flowers can be used for their antibacterial properties with no adverse side effects.

Burdock (Arctium lappa)
Burdock has antibacterial properties and a tea made from it can be used as a household cleaner and also as a skin and face wash. Apply the cooled tea to the skin with a clean facecloth, and rinse in cool water.

Butcher's broom (Ruscus aculeatus)
The butcher's broom plant gets its name because it was once used by butchers in Europe to clean their chopping blocks due to its powerful antibacterial and antimicrobial properties.

Butterbur (Petasites hybridus)
Butterbur is a perennial wild flower/herb with lilac-pink flower heads and large rhubarb-like leaves. The leaves contain alkaloids and are known to have been used as a medicinal and cleansing herb as far back as the Iron Age.

Chinese rhubarb root (Rheum palmatum, Rheum rhaponticum, Rheum palmatum)
Chinese rhubarb root has powerful antibacterial properties.

Cinnamon (Cinnamomum zeylanicum)
Cinnamon is a potent antibacterial and antifungal cleansing herb.

Cloves (Syzygium aromaticum, Egenia caryophyllata)
Aromatic crushed cloves are antiseptic, antiviral and antifungal.

Coconut (Cocos nucifera)
The flesh, milk and water of coconuts are antibacterial, antifungal, antiparasitic and antiviral.

Coriander (Coriandrum sativum)
Also known as cilantro, this aromatic herb can eliminate unpleasant odours and it contains the antibacterial compound dodecenal in both the seed and leaves that kills *Salmonella*. In addition to dodecenal, eight other antibiotic compounds are found in coriander leaves that can kill food-borne bacteria.

Cumin seeds (Cuminum cyminum)
The powerful cleansing properties of cumin are in its volatile oil which is a rich source of thymol.

Dandelion root (Taraxacum officinale)
The root of the dandelion has powerful antimicrobial properties. Boil chopped pieces of the root for 15 minutes, then strain and use as a natural cleaner.

Dill (Anethum graveolens)
Dill contains powerful antibacterial volatile oils.

Eucalyptus (Eucalyptus globulus labill)
The leaves and oil from the eucalyptus tree have very powerful antiseptic properties and its aromatic oil can help bronchial and sinus congestion that may be due to pollutants in the air.

Fagara (Zanthoxyloides)
It has been found, in scientific studies, that the alcoholic extracts of

the root-bark of fagara possess considerable antibacterial activity and may even be effective against Lyme disease and venereal bacteria such as gonorrhoea and syphilis.

False daisy (Eclipta alba)
False daisy has powerful antibacterial and antiseptic properties that make it highly effective as a household cleaner.

Fennel seeds (Foeniculum vulgare)
Fennel leaves and seeds contain volatile oils with powerful antimicrobial effects. Fennel is very easy to grow from seed.

Golden rod (Solidago canadensis, Solidago odora, Solidago virgaurea)
Golden rod has powerful antibacterial, antifungal and antiviral properties.

Golden seal (Hydrastis Canadensis)
Golden seal is a herb that has been used for centuries as a powerful antibacterial cleanser.

Honeysuckle flowers (Lonicera pericylmenum, Lonicera aponica)
Honeysuckle flowers have antibiotic properties and can add a pleasant fragrance to cleaners.

Lavender (Lavandula angustifolia)

Easily grown in the UK garden, lavender leaves and flowers can be used for their antibacterial properties with no adverse side effects.

Lemon balm (Melissa officinalis)

Also known as melissa oil, this herb has powerful antibacterial and antiviral properties.

Lemongrass (Cymbopogon)

Citronella oil is derived from the leaves and stems of lemongrass and is an excellent insect repellent, especially against mosquitoes, and can also be used as an effective household cleaner without harsh chemical additives. To grow lemongrass in the home, buy a few stalks and place the bulb end in water and allow to soak until roots form (this may take anywhere from two weeks to a month). Once the lemongrass has developed roots ½ to 1 inch long, plant in a pot with lots of rich soil. Lemongrass likes sun and warm temperatures, so keep it indoors as a houseplant and place on a south-facing windowsill.

Marigold (Calendula officinalis)

Marigolds have powerful antiseptic properties and can help to repel insects when grown in a pot in the home.

Marjoram (Origanum majorana)

Marjoram contains volatile antibacterial and antiseptic oils when used like a tea as a natural cleaner.

Mint (Mentha arvensis)

Mint is antibacterial, antiseptic and antifungal and imparts a pleasant fragrance when used as a natural cleaner.

Moringa (Moringa oleifera)

Moringa seeds can be used as a powerful cleaner due to their antibiotic and antifungal properties.

Nasturtium (Tropaeolum majus)

Nasturtium leaves or petals can be ground up using a mortar and pestle to make a cleaning paste that has antibiotic, antiseptic and antifungal properties.

Nettles (Urtica dioica)

A tea made from the common stinging nettle has powerful antibacterial and antifungal properties and, because it grows so prolifically everywhere, it makes an excellent natural alternative to use as a surface cleaner.

Nutmeg (Myristica fragrans)

Because of its antibacterial properties, nutmeg makes an effective cleaner along with its pleasant aroma that is said to improve the cognitive function of the brain and enhance the mood.

Oleander leaf (Nerium indicum)

The oleander leaf has strong volatile oils which can be used as an effective cleaner in the home as well as a powerful insecticide.

NOTE: Care must be taken with this plant as one raw leaf has enough poison in it to kill a small child, as well as any pet.

Olive leaf (Olea europaea)

Research suggests that olive leaf may be a true antiviral compound in ways not addressed by pharmaceutical antibiotics and for this reason it is a good addition as a natural cleaning substance. Olive leaf's broad killing power includes an ability to interfere with critical amino acid production of viruses by preventing virus shredding, budding or assembly at the cell membrane. It is especially useful in combating the herpes viruses that can be so easily contracted, and the hepatitis virus amongst others.

Oregano (Origanum compactum)

Oregano contains carvacrol which fights food poisoning bacteria, the *Toxoplasmosis gondii* parasite, norovirus (winter vomiting disease) and the intestinal infection *Helicobacter pylori*. Steep a handful of oregano leaves in boiled water until it turns cold, then remove the leaves and add to a spray bottle to disinfect surfaces. The root of the oregano plant contains berberine which is a compound that is highly effective against fungi and protozoa as well as bacteria and viruses.

Paico leaf (Chenopodium ambrosoides)

Paico leaves have powerful compounds that can kill germs, worms and parasites. Hanging branches of paico inside or having a plant growing in the home also repels insects.

NOTE: Pregnant and breast feeding women should avoid using the paico herb.

Parsley (Petroselinum crispum)

Parsley is especially useful for killing human head lice but can also be used to clean the home. Steep a handful of parsley leaves in a cupful of boiled water until it turns cold, then remove the leaves and add to a spray bottle to disinfect surfaces or use as a shampoo.

Passion flower (Passiflora incarnata)

Passion flower leaves contain an alkaloid known as passicol, which kills a wide range of bacteria, moulds and yeasts. Steep a handful of passion flower leaves in boiled water until it turns cold then remove the leaves and add to a spray bottle to disinfect surfaces. It can also be used as an effective shampoo against dandruff.

Pau d'arco (Tabebuia serratifolia, Tabebuia impetiginosa)

Pau d'Arco is an Amazonian tree that is highly effective against bacteria and fungi and also works against various parasites, including those that cause: malaria, schistosomiasis and trypanosomiasis. Antiviral properties have also been displayed against several viruses, including vesicular stomatitis virus, shortened to VSV; it is therefore a good herb to use as a household cleaner.

Peppercorns (Piper nigrum)

Because of its antibacterial properties, pepper is used to preserve food. Add it to other steeped herbs for extra cleaning power in the kitchen and bathroom.

Peppermint (Mentha piperita)

The antiseptic properties of menthol in peppermint make it ideal as a surface cleaner and it provides a fresh minty smell. Steep a handful of peppermint leaves in boiled water until it turns cold, then remove the leaves and add to a spray bottle to disinfect surfaces. Peppermint oil will also deter ants, mice and rats as they detest the smell.

Perilla leaves (Perilla frutescens)

The perilla plant is a member of the *Lamiaceae* or mint family and has powerful antibiotic properties. It can also be used as an effective antidote to food poisoning bacteria so is useful as a cleaner in the kitchen.
NOTE: Perilla leaves are poisonous to cattle.

Phyllanthus amarus (Phyllanthus niruri)

This world-renowned botanical herb has been used for its antibacterial and antiviral properties for the past 2000 years. It makes an effective cleaner to use in the home.

Pine (Pinus aphremphous, Pinus koraiensis, Pinus sabin-iana, Pinus sibirica, Pinus sylvestris, Pinus taeda)

Pine needles contain strong volatile oils that are antibacterial and its scent provides a pleasant aroma for the home when used as a cleaner. To prepare a pine needle solution, pick a handful of pine needles. Remove the papery brown coverings at the ends and chop the needles into ½ inch/1 centimetre pieces. Pour a cup of very hot (but not boiling) water over a tablespoon of chopped needles. Let the infusion steep for at least 20 minutes. Strain and place in a spray bottle.

Purslane (Portulaca oleracea, Portulaca sativa)
Purslane is a very common weed that grows wild and has powerful antibiotic properties even against the *Treponema pallidum* bacteria that is responsible for syphilis.

Red clover (Trifolium pratense)
Red clover is one of the few sources of deoxybenzoins which are polyphenols that have highly effective antimicrobial and antiviral properties, making it a good choice as a household cleaner.

Red raspberry seeds (Ubus idaeus)
The ellagitannin found in the crushed seeds of red raspberry seeds has been found to be a powerful destroyer of microbes and parasites. It also has very strong antibacterial, antifungal and antiviral properties.

Rose geranium (Pelargonium graveolens)
Neem leaves, rosemary and lavender contain natural insecticidal properties and these herbs together with the aromatic and

antimicrobial herbs such as tea tree oil and rose geranium have the ability to eliminate external parasites, including pubic lice, and prevent re-infestation. Because of this they all make good cleaners for the home.

Rosemary (Rosmarinus officinalis)
Rosemary has highly effective antibacterial, antifungal and antiseptic properties. Steep a handful of rosemary leaves in hot but not boiling water until it turns cold, then remove the leaves and add to a spray bottle to disinfect surfaces.

NOTE: Avoid rosemary if suffering from high blood pressure, pregnant or breastfeeding.

Sage (Salvia officinalis)
Sage is a useful and easy pot herb to grow in the home and can be used as an antibacterial and antiseptic cleaner.

NOTE: Sage should be avoided if pregnant or suffering from epilepsy.

Sarsaparilla (Smilax longiflora)
Sarsaparilla is an Amazonian plant with effective antibacterial and antiseptic properties. It is said to be particularly good at eliminating the syphilis bacterium.

Savoury (summer savoury, Satureja hortensis, winter savoury, Ssatureja montana)
Savoury (USA spelling: 'savory') is an aromatic herb similar in

structure to thyme but with its own unique aroma and properties. Thymol, one of the important essential oils in savoury, has scientifically been found to have antiseptic and anti-fungal properties. The carvacrol in savoury inhibits the growth of several bacteria strains like *E. coli*, and *Bacillus cereus*.

Scutellaria (Scutellaria baicalensis)

The root of the scutellaria plant, which has been used in Chinese medicine for a very long time as the herb Huang-qin, is extremely effective for killing contagious 'flu-like viruses. There is really no better anti-infection agent in the herb kingdom to use as a protective cleaner in the home.

Spearmint (Mentha spicata)

The essential oil, menthol, in spearmint has antibacterial properties and is a useful substance for a household cleaner as well as in toothpaste and mouth refreshers. It is one of the few herbs safe to use whilst pregnant.

Stephania root (Stephania tetrandra)

Stephania has powerful antibacterial compounds that are effective even against the bacteria that cause Lyme disease and syphilis.

Sumac (Rhus coriaria)

Sumac has antibacterial properties and a solution of sumac and water can be used to safely wash bacteria from vegetables and fruits as well as kitchen surfaces. The antimicrobial properties of sumac are attributed to the presence of methyl gallic acid, gallic acid and other compounds.

NOTE: Poisonous white sumac with drooping white berry clusters is highly toxic. The sumac that is safe to use has red berries. Sumac is related to cashews, mangos and poison ivy. Anyone who is so sensitive to this family cannot eat cashews or mangoes and should avoid sumac too.

Tarragon (Artemisia dranunculus)

Tarragon is an age old herb that can fight food poisoning bacteria so is useful as a kitchen surface cleaner.

Tea tree oil (Melaleuca alternifolia)

Tea tree oil is extracted from the leaves of the Australian *Melaleuca alternafolia* tree that has powerful antibacterial, antifungal and antiviral qualities so can be used to effectively clean the home without leaving toxic residues behind. It can also be used in the bath as a body wash.

Thyme and lemon Thyme (Thymus vulgaris, Thymus citriodorus)

Thyme contains thymol, which acts as a disinfectant. Steep a handful of thyme leaves in hot but not boiling water until it turns cold, then remove the leaves and add the liquid to a spray bottle to disinfect surfaces.

Vanilla (*Vanilla planifolia*)

Pleasantly fragrant rich vanilla beans are the pods or fruits obtained from a tropical climbing orchid that have antibacterial properties so make a pleasantly aromatic cleaner for the home.

How to use white vinegar as a cleaner and polish

Method

1. Purchase spray bottles from a hardware store and fill one with boiled water and four tables spoons of white vinegar. Shake well and leave to stand whilst chopping the herbs you have chosen to use from the list above.
2. Take a handful of the herbs, leaves and, using sharp scissors, chop into small pieces into a mug.
3. Pour boiled hot (but not boiling) water over them and leave to steep for at least 20 minutes. Strain the juice into a jug.
4. Empty the water and vinegar solution from one spray bottle into another for step 6 and fill the original spray bottle with the strained herb juice. Top up with cold boiled water. Shake the spray bottle of natural cleaning solution before each use.
5. Spray surfaces and leave them wet for at least one minute before wiping them down.
6. Then use the spray bottle filled with clean water and four tablespoons of white vinegar to polish dry the surfaces of sinks, baths, showers, toilets, cookers, microwaves, washers

and dryers and the inside of refrigerators and freezers. The shiny polished surface this creates will make it harder for mould and bacteria to cling to. Two tablespoons of any steeped aromatic herb solution from the list above, such as lavender, can be added to the polish solution for a pleasant toxin-free fragrance.

White vinegar is very effective at killing *E. coli*, *Salmonella* and *Shigella* bacteria. It's good for everything from soaking vegetables to washing the floors. Vinegar is 99% effective at killing all germs if left on any surface for at least 60 seconds, and using it leaves a nice shine

Use a spray bottle filled with clean water and two tablespoons of white vinegar to polish dry the surfaces of sinks, baths, showers, toilets, cookers, microwaves, washers and dryers and the inside of refrigerators and freezers, after they have been cleaned with a wet cloth. This will prevent the growth of mould and bacteria and deter ant infestations as it disrupts the pathways which they use to find food.

NOTE: Use vinegar on any surface except natural stone as its acidic qualities can etch materials like granite.

NOTE: As there are no added preservatives, the herbal solutions described must be kept in a cool dark place. Adding a tablespoon of white vinegar, coconut water or lemon juice can preserve them for longer. It will be known when they are no longer usable by the unpleasant smell which is not harmful but means their cleaning properties have deteriorated. To make a stronger solution, add two cups of the steeped herb solution or mix and match different herbs as desired.

Index

Aglaonema crispum, 34
Aloe barbadensi, 91
aloe vera, 20, 91
amaryllis, 80
ammonia, 8
angel's trumpets, 80
anise seeds, 91
areca palm, 22
avocado, 81
azalea, 24
bamboo palm, 26
banana fig, 28
banana tree, 30
Barberton daisy, 48
basil, 91
basil, Holy 52
bay leaves, 92
beeswax polish, 17
Begonia semperflorens, 74
benzene, 9
bergamot, 92

blue vervain, 92
borage, 92
Boston fern, 32
Brassaia actinophylla, 70
brominated flame retardants, 9
burdock, 92
butane, 9
butcher's broom, 93
butterbur, 93
cannabis, 81
castor bean, 82
Chamaedorea sefritzii, 26
chemical combinations, 10
Chinese evergreen, 34
Chinese money tree, 72
Chinese rhubarb root, 93
chives, 82
chlorophyll, 5
Chlorophytum comosum, 68
Chrysalidocarpus lutescens, 22
Chrysantheium morifolium, 36

chrysanthemum, 36
cinnamon, 93
citronella, 96
cleaning products, 10
cloves, 93
coconut, 93
coriander, 94
corn cane, 38
cumin seeds, 94
cyanide (in fruit stones, pips
    etc), 16
cyclamen, 82
daffodils, 82
dandelion root, 94
decane, 11
devil's ivy, 40
devil's trumpet, 83
dill, 94
Dracaena deremensis, 72
Dracaena marginata, 42
Dracaena massangeana, 38
dragon tree, 42
dwarf pygmy data palm, 44
English ivy, 46
ethylene, 11
eucalyptus, 94

fagara, 94
false daisy, 95
fennel seeds, 95
Ficus benjamina, 76
Ficus elastic, 66
Ficus maeleilandii alii, 28
Ficus robusta, 66
Formaldehyde, 11
fox gloves, 83
fungus gnats, 86
garlic, 82
gerbera, 48
Gerbera jamesonii, 48
glycosides, 82
golden pothos, 40
golden rod, 95
golden seal, 95
grayanotoxins, 24
heart leaf plant, 50
Hedera helix, 46
holy basil, 52
honeysuckle, 95
hops, 83
hyacinths, 82
Japanese andromeda, 83
Japanese yew, 83

jimson weed, 83
kalanchoe, 84
Kimberly queen fern, 54
lady palm, 56
laurel, 80
lavender, 96
leeks, 82
lemon balm, 96
lemongrass, 96
lilies, 84
lily of the valley, 84
lily turf, 58
Liriope spicata, 58
marigold, 96
marjoram, 96
Melissa officinalis, 96
mint, 96
moringa, 97
mother in law's tongue, 60
moth orchid, 62
Muso oriana, 30
nasturtium, 97
*Nephrolepis exaltata
bostoniensis*, 32
Nephrolepsis obliterate, 54
nettles, 97

nonane, 12
nutmeg, 97
Ocimum tenuiflorum, 52
oleander, 84
olive leaf, 98
onions, 82
oregano, 98
paico leaf, 98
paint, 13
parsley, 98
passion flower, 98
pau d'arco, 98
PCBs, 13
Peperomia obtusifolia, 66
peppercorns, 100
peppermint, 100
perilla leaves, 100
Phalaenopsis amabilis, 62
Philodendron hederaceum, 50
Philodendron oxycardium, 50
Phoenix roebelenii, 44
Phyllanthus amarus, 100
pine, 100
polychlorinated biphenyls, 13
purslane, 101
radon, 14

red clover, 101
red raspberry seeds, 101
Rhapis excelsa, 56
Rhododendrom simsii, 24
rhubarb, 84
rose geranium, 101
rosemary, 102
rubber plant, 66
sage, 102
sago palm plant, 85
Sansevieria trifasciata Laurentii, 60
sarsaparilla, 102
savoury, 102
Scindapsus aures
scutellaria, 103
shamrock, 85
snake plant, 60
Spathiphyllum wallisii, 64
spearmint, 103
spider plant, 68
stephania root, 103

styrene, 16
sumac, 103
sweet heart plant, 50
tarragon, 104
tea tree oil, 104
thyme, 104
tobacco, 16
toluene, 16
trichloroethylene, 17
tulips, 82
umbrella tree, 70
vanilla, 105
vinegar, 105
warneck dracaena, 72
wax begonia, 74
wax candles, 17
weeping fig, 76
xylene, 18, 79

About the Author

Nat H Hawes SNHS Dip. (Advanced Nutrition and Sports Nutrition) has been studying and researching natural remedies, nutrients and the power of traditional foods and medicines since 2003. She believes, based on this research, that, unless nutrient deficiencies are tested for properly and shown to be present, extracted nutrient supplements are unnecessary and can do more harm than good. Natural and unrefined whole foods will provide the body with all the fuel it requires to function correctly and recover from most common ailments. She can be contacted through the following:

- Website: naturecures.co.uk
- Email: health@naturecures.co.uk
- Mobile: +44 (0)7966 519844